GRADE

04

VIOLIN

Pieces for Trinity College London
Exams 2020-2023

Audio available:
- CD available to purchase from **trinitycollege.com/shop**
- Stream or purchase from Amazon, Google Play, iTunes, Spotify and other platforms
- Practice tools – check **trinitycollege.com/music-books** for new developments

Published by
Trinity College London Press Ltd
trinitycollege.com

Registered in England
Company no. 09726123

© Copyright 2019 Trinity College London Press Ltd
First impression, June 2019

Cover image courtesy of Klaus Ludwig Clement, clement-geigenbau.com
Printed in England by Caligraving Ltd

The Crystal Spring

Trad.

arr. K & D Blackwell

Passamezzo

Diego Ortiz
(ca. 1510)
arr. Huws Jones

[This page has been left blank to facilitate page turns]

Sarabanda

from *Sonata VIII*, op. 5

Arcangelo Corelli
(1653-1713)
arr. Cornick

quasi acoustic bass

Omit the repeats in the exam.

Gavotta

from *Sonata in A*, op. 5 no. 2, RV 30

Antonio Vivaldi
(1678-1741)

Omit the repeats in the exam.

TRINITY
COLLEGE LONDON PRESS

GRADE

04
VIOLIN

**Pieces for Trinity College London
Exams 2020–2023**

Audio available:
- CD available to purchase from **trinitycollege.com/shop**
- Stream or purchase from Amazon, Google Play, iTunes, Spotify and other platforms
- Practice tools – check **trinitycollege.com/music-books** for new developments

Published by
Trinity College London Press Ltd
trinitycollege.com

Registered in England
Company no. 09726123

Cover image courtesy of Klaus Ludwig Clement, clement-geigenbau.com
Printed in England by Caligraving Ltd

The Crystal Spring

Trad.

arr. K & D Blackwell

Passamezzo

Diego Ortiz
(ca. 1510)
arr. Huws Jones

[This page has been left blank to facilitate page turns]

Sarabanda

from *Sonata VIII*, op. 5

Arcangelo Corelli
(1653-1713)
arr. Cornick

Omit the repeats in the exam.

Gavotta

from *Sonata in A*, op. 5 no. 2, RV 30

Antonio Vivaldi
(1678-1741)

Omit the repeats in the exam.

Allegro

3rd movt from *Violin Sonata in D minor*

Michel Corrette
(1707-1795)

Omit the repeats in the exam.

La captive

no. 1 from *Three Compositions*, op. 40

Amy Beach
(1867-1944)

Omit the repeats in the exam. *Ignore 2nd time instruction in the exam (play *mf*).

[This page has been left blank to facilitate page turns]

El choclo

Norman Tailor
(b. 1928)

Omit the repeats in the exam.

Gigue

Joseph Bodin de Boismortier
(1689-1755)

Omit the repeats in the exam.

[This page has been left blank to facilitate page turns]

Allegro

3rd movt from *Violin Sonata in D minor*

Michel Corrette
(1707-1795)

Omit the repeats in the exam.

La captive

no. 1 from *Three Compositions*, op. 40

Amy Beach
(1867-1944)

Omit the repeats in the exam. *Ignore 2nd time instruction in the exam (play **mf**).

El choclo

Norman Tailor
(b. 1928)

Omit the repeats in the exam.